My New Brother

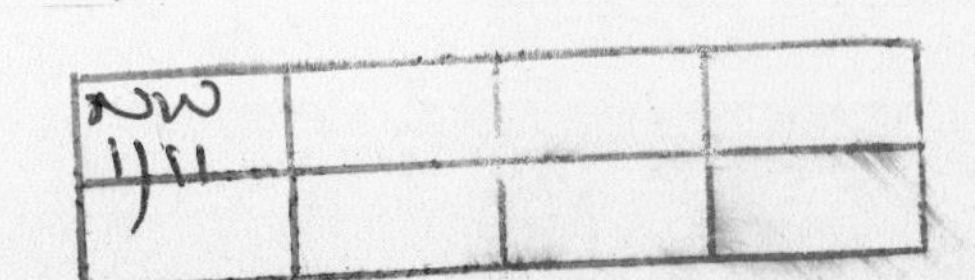

First published in 2010
by Wayland

Wayland
338 Euston Road
London NW1 3BH

Wayland Australia
Level 17/207 Kent Street
Sydney, NSW 2000

Series Editor: Louise John
Editor: Katie Powell
Design: D.R.ink
Consultant: Shirley Bickler
Photographer: Andy Crawford

A CIP catalogue record for this book is available from the British Library.

ISBN 9780750263788

Printed in China

Wayland is a division of Hachette Children's Books,
an Hachette UK Company

www.hachette.co.uk

With thanks to Jessica Aston, Austin Harries,
Amelia and Angela John

Contents

This is Austin

I have a new baby brother.

His name is Austin.
Austin is six weeks old.

Austin is born

Grandma and I were in the park
when Mum called me on the phone.

Austin is born

Grandma and I were in the park when Mum called me on the phone.

As he got bigger, Mum got bigger, too. She said, "I hope this baby comes out soon. I am getting so big!"

Austin grows

At first Austin grew in Mum's tummy.

His name is Austin.
Austin is six weeks old.

She said, “Amelia, the baby has come out. You have a new baby brother!”

At the hospital

Grandma and I went to the hospital to see Mum and Dad.

My brother was in a little cot.
He had a present for me.
It was a toy camera.

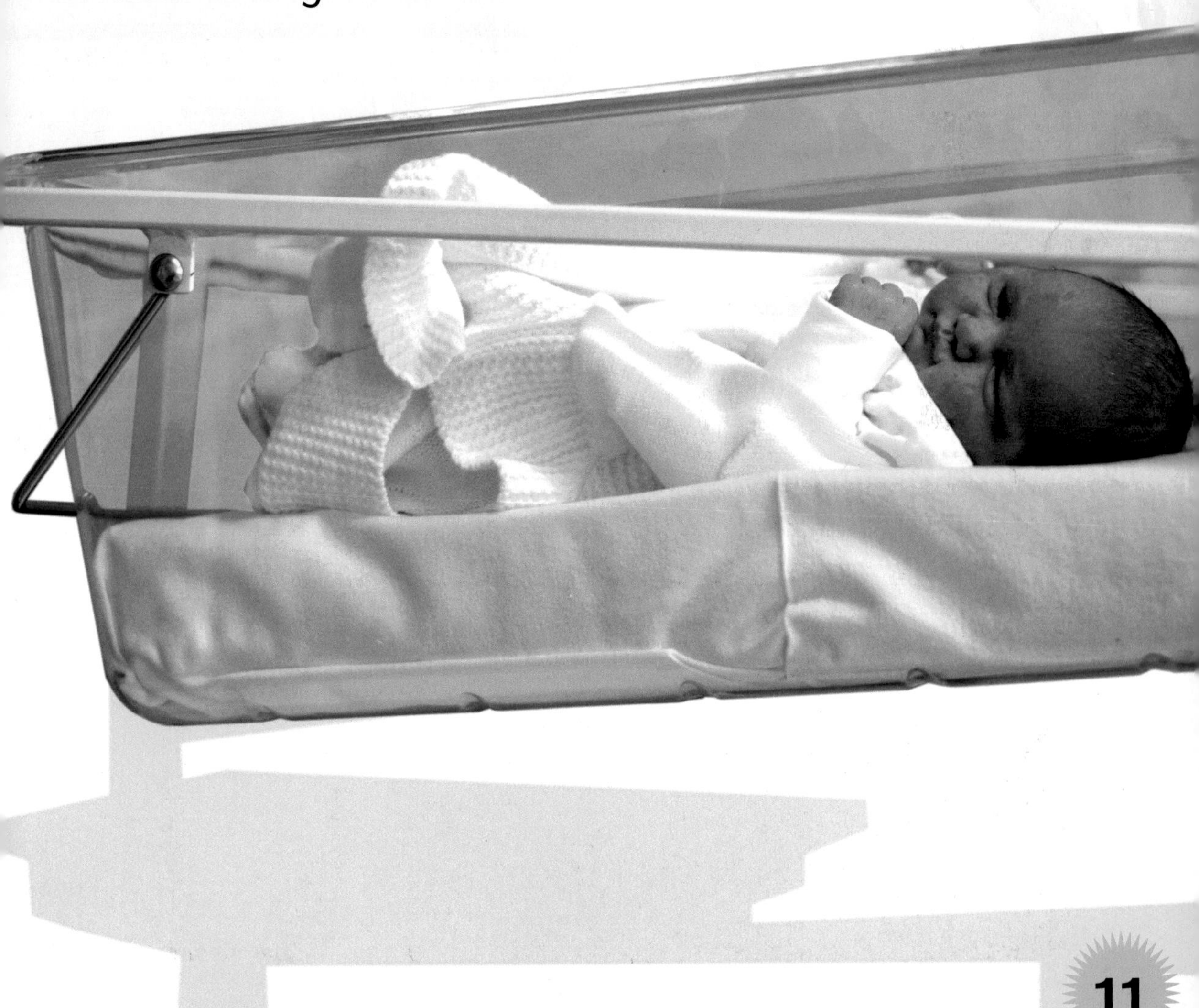

Austin comes home

The next day Mum and Austin came home. Mum said, "Do you want to hold your brother?"

She put Austin on my lap
but he did not look at me.

Austin's room

Austin has my old bedroom.
He sleeps in my old cot.

I have the big bedroom now.
I sleep in a bed.

Austin cries

My baby brother is not much fun.
He sleeps and eats and he cries a lot!

I don't like the noise.
Grandma says, "You did this
when you were a baby!"

Austin smiles

I gave Austin his milk today.
He looked at me when he was
drinking it.

Then he gave me a big smile.
I think he likes me.

Austin and me

I will look after Austin.
I will keep him safe.

When he is big I will play with him.
I'm glad I have a baby brother.

Tell the story

These photos will help you tell the story of my new brother. Can you put them in the right order?

START READING is a series of highly enjoyable books for beginner readers. **The books have been carefully graded to match the Book Bands widely used in schools.** This enables readers to be sure they choose books that match their own reading ability.

Look out for the Band colour on the book in our Start Reading logo.

The Bands are:

START READING books can be read independently or shared with an adult. They promote the enjoyment of reading through satisfying stories and non-fiction narratives, which are supported by fun illustrations and photographs.

Claire Llewellyn has written many books for children. Some of them are about real things like animals and the Moon, others are storybooks. Claire has two children, but they are getting too big for her books now. She hopes you will enjoy reading them instead!